contents

C000000152

Life Processes and Liv...

Materials and their Properties   14 - 22

Physical Processes   23 - 33

THE
HUMAN SKELETON

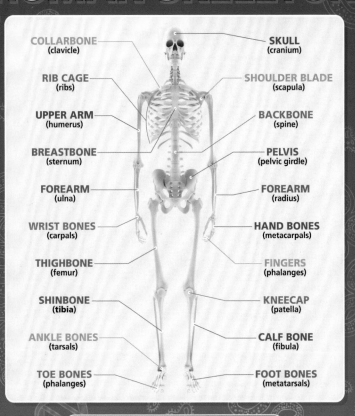

COLLARBONE
(clavicle)

RIB CAGE
(ribs)

UPPER ARM
(humerus)

BREASTBONE
(sternum)

FOREARM
(ulna)

WRIST BONES
(carpals)

THIGHBONE
(femur)

SHINBONE
(tibia)

ANKLE BONES
(tarsals)

TOE BONES
(phalanges)

SKULL
(cranium)

SHOULDER BLADE
(scapula)

BACKBONE
(spine)

PELVIS
(pelvic girdle)

FOREARM
(radius)

HAND BONES
(metacarpals)

FINGERS
(phalanges)

KNEECAP
(patella)

CALF BONE
(fibula)

FOOT BONES
(metatarsals)

WHY DO WE HAVE A SKELETON IN OUR BODY?

There are three important reasons:

SUPPORT

The skeleton supports our body. Without this support we would not be able to stand upright.

MOVEMENT

The skeleton has joints where tendons join muscles to bones. This enables us to move.

PROTECTION

The skeleton helps to protect delicate internal organs from injury.

DID YOU KNOW?
The average human adult skeleton has **213** bones.

JOINTS

A joint is the point where two or more bones meet. There are three main types of joints:

Immovable	**Partially Movable**	**Freely Movable**
(Fibrous)	(Cartilaginous)	(Synovial)
Joints where there is little or no movement.	Joints where there is a limited range of movement.	Joints where there is free movement.

Freely Movable Joints

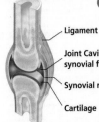

- Ligament
- Joint Cavity (contains synovial fluid)
- Synovial membrane
- Cartilage

Bones at freely movable (synovial) joints are held together by ligaments.

The ends of bones are covered in cartilage to aid movement and stop the bones from rubbing together.

Synovial fluid reduces friction at joints, allowing them to move more freely.

Types of Joints

Hinge

Provides movement in one plane; backward and forward.

Examples: fingers, toes, knees, and elbows

Ball & Socket

Provides 360° rotation and movement in all planes.

This joint provides the greatest range of movement.

Examples: hip and shoulder

Condyloid

Provides movement in two planes; backward and forward, and side to side.

Examples: wrist

Gliding

Provides limited movement in all directions.

Examples: vertebrae and carpel bones in the hand

Pivot

Provides rotatory movements only.

Examples: arm (radius and ulna)

Saddle

Provides movement in two planes; backward and forward, and side to side.

Examples: thumb

MUSCLES

There are over 600 muscles in the human body. There are three main types of muscle:

Cardiac

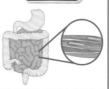

- Involuntarily controlled
- Found in the walls of the heart
- Do not fatigue

Smooth

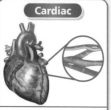

- Involuntarily controlled
- Found within walls of hollow organs such as the stomach and intestines

Skeletal

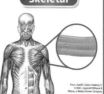

From L/MARTE, Colour Anatomy 2
© 2004, Lippincott Williams &
Wilkins, a Wolters Kluwer Company

- Voluntarily controlled
- Found throughout body
- Attached to bones by tendons

Skeletal Muscles

Muscles contract to pull bones, but they cannot push them. To achieve movement in two directions, muscles must work in pairs. Antagonistic muscles are pairs of muscles that work together to create movement.

The biceps and triceps are antagonistic muscles that work together to bend and straighten your arm.

Straight Arm

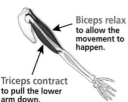

Biceps relax to allow the movement to happen.

Triceps contract to pull the lower arm down.

Bent Arm

Triceps relax to allow the movement to happen.

Biceps contract to pull the lower arm up.

The hamstrings and quadriceps are antagonistic muscles that work together to bend and straighten your leg.

Straight Leg

Quadriceps contract to pull the lower leg down.

Hamstrings relax to allow the movement to happen.

Bent Leg

Quadriceps relax to allow the movement to happen.

Hamstrings contract to pull the lower leg up.

daydream

THE HEART
AND CIRCULATION

The heart is an organ that pumps blood around the body to deliver oxygen and nutrients, and to remove waste, including carbon dioxide.

VEINS carry blood **TO** the heart from other organs.

VALVES open and close in sequence to allow blood to flow through the heart in one direction only.

CHAMBERS have contracting walls to squeeze blood to the arteries. There are four chambers in the heart.

ARTERIES carry blood **AWAY** from the heart to other organs.

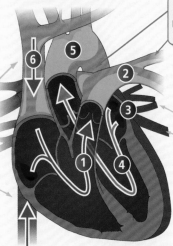

Arteries carrying blood to the body

Veins carrying blood from the body

Veins carrying blood from the body

Deoxygenated blood from the body

RIGHT SIDE

LEFT SIDE

Oxygenated blood from the lungs

1 The bottom-right chamber of the heart contracts, pushing blood containing carbon dioxide out through an artery.

2 The blood travels to the lungs where the carbon dioxide is exchanged for oxygen from the air that has been inhaled.

3 The blood then travels from the lungs back to the heart throughout the veins.

4 The top-left chamber of the heart contracts, pushing blood into the bottom-left chamber. Then, the bottom-left chamber contracts and pushes blood out through an artery.

5 The blood is transported around the body to deliver oxygen for energy production.

6 During energy production, carbon dioxide and other waste products are created. These are transported back to the heart and the process starts again.

daydream education

BREATHING

Breathing is the process that controls the movement of air in and out of the lungs.
We breathe to get oxygen into our bodies, and carbon dioxide out.

THE LUNGS

The lungs are the main organ of the respiratory system.

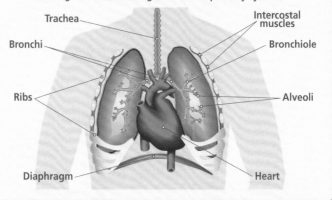

- Trachea
- Bronchi
- Ribs
- Diaphragm
- Intercostal muscles
- Bronchiole
- Alveoli
- Heart

INHALING

We inhale, or breathe in, to supply our cells with oxygen. Nearly every bodily function uses oxygen as its source of energy.

Chest volume increases as air is sucked into the lungs.

The muscles between the ribs contract to expand the rib cage.

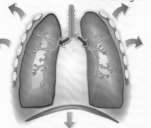

The diaphragm contracts and moves down.

EXHALING

We exhale, or breathe out, to remove carbon dioxide from our bodies. Carbon dioxide is produced when cells create energy during respiration.

Chest volume decreases as air is forced out of the lungs.

The muscles between the ribs relax to reduce chest volume.

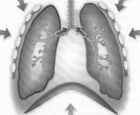

The diaphragm relaxes and moves up.

visit www.daydreameducation.co.uk for more information

DIGESTION

The food you eat is broken down and this is called digestion.

THE DIGESTIVE SYSTEM

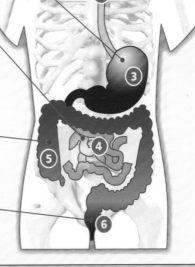

MOUTH

1 Food is chewed and swallowed.

Saliva contains an enzyme that breaks down starch into glucose.

OESOPHAGUS

2 Food passes down the oesophagus to the stomach.

STOMACH

3 The muscle walls of the stomach produce gastric juices that contain the protease enzyme.

This breaks down protein to amino acid.

SMALL INTESTINE

4 The small intestine produces amylase, protease and lipase enzymes to break down additional protein, carbohydrate and fats.

Digestion is then complete and food is absorbed into the bloodstream.

LARGE INTESTINE

5 Indigestible food goes to the large intestine.

Water is absorbed and the remaining food becomes faeces.

RECTUM

6 Faeces are stored in the rectum and leave the body through the anus.

THE EYE

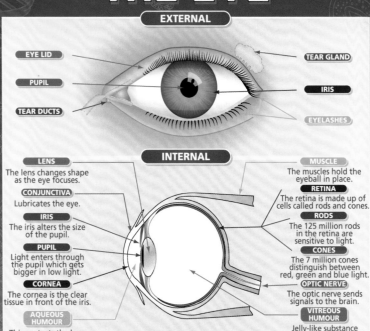

EXTERNAL

- **EYE LID**
- **PUPIL**
- **TEAR DUCTS**
- **TEAR GLAND**
- **IRIS**
- **EYELASHES**

INTERNAL

LENS
The lens changes shape as the eye focuses.

CONJUNCTIVA
Lubricates the eye.

IRIS
The iris alters the size of the pupil.

PUPIL
Light enters through the pupil which gets bigger in low light.

CORNEA
The cornea is the clear tissue in front of the iris.

AQUEOUS HUMOUR
This protects the lens.

MUSCLE
The muscles hold the eyeball in place.

RETINA
The retina is made up of cells called rods and cones.

RODS
The 125 million rods in the retina are sensitive to light.

CONES
The 7 million cones distinguish between red, green and blue light.

OPTIC NERVE
The optic nerve sends signals to the brain.

VITREOUS HUMOUR
Jelly-like substance which fills the eyeball.

HOW WE SEE

The eye is amazing. It can see from a few millimetres to millions of kilometres away.

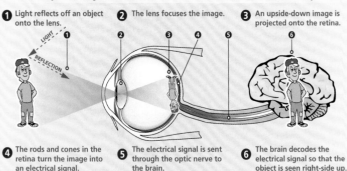

❶ Light reflects off an object onto the lens.

❷ The lens focuses the image.

❸ An upside-down image is projected onto the retina.

❹ The rods and cones in the retina turn the image into an electrical signal.

❺ The electrical signal is sent through the optic nerve to the brain.

❻ The brain decodes the electrical signal so that the object is seen right-side up.

Did you know?
There are 125 million rods and 7 million cones in the eye.

NUTRITION

The energy and nutrients needed by your body to grow and stay healthy come from the air you breathe, the food you eat and the fluids you drink.

A BALANCED DIET

A guideline for a healthy diet is shown below.

FRUIT AND VEGETABLES

A great source of fibre and a variety of vitamins and minerals.

Generally low in fat.

RICE, BREAD, PASTA AND OTHER STARCHY FOODS

High in carbohydrates.

Wholegrain varieties are a great source of fibre and protein.

MEAT, FISH, EGG AND BEANS

A great source of protein, iron and zinc.

Choose lean cuts of meat to reduce fat intake.

MILK AND DAIRY FOODS

Can be high in fat.

A great source of calcium and protein.

FATTY AND SUGARY FOODS
High in fat and sugar.

UNDERSTANDING NUTRITION

All of the foods you eat are made up of the following nutrients.

Fats

Saturated and trans fats increase your risk of heart disease, diabetes and other health problems.
However, not all fats are bad for you. The right fats can help lower cholesterol and fight fatigue.

Good	Bad

Be careful! Many fat-free foods are high in calories and can result in weight gain.

Carbohydrates

Carbohydrates are your body's main source of energy.
Complex carbs help protect against heart disease and diabetes, whereas simple carbs digest quickly and cause spikes in blood sugar levels.

Complex	Simple

For a healthier diet, replace refined (white) bread, pasta and rice with wholegrain varieties.

Protein

Proteins are used by the body for growth and maintenance. Sources include:

Vitamins and Minerals

Vitamins and minerals help keep the body healthy. Sources include:

FOOD CHAINS

Living things depend on other living things for food to make energy.

THE FOOD CHAIN

Some living things, known as **producers**, make their own food from the sun's energy. Other living things, known as **consumers**, receive energy by consuming other organisms.

PRODUCERS — **CONSUMERS**

Producers
Plants make their own food from the sun's energy.

Primary Consumers
Animals that only eat producers.

Secondary Consumers
Animals that eat primary consumers.

Tertiary Consumers
Animals that eat secondary consumers.

ENERGY TRANSFER

Energy is transferred along food chains. The amount of energy transferred reduces from one stage to the next. The majority of the energy is used by the consumer to move, grow and keep warm.

Energy from sun 100%

Producer

10%

Primary Consumer

1%

Secondary Consumer

0.1%

 Transferred 90%   9%   0.9%
Used/lost

TYPES OF CONSUMER

Carnivores Animals that eat other animals.			
Top Carnivores Animals that are not eaten by other living things.			
Herbivores Animals that eat only plants.			
Omnivores Animals that eat plants and other living things.			

PHOTOSYNTHESIS

Photosynthesis is the process by which plants and other organisms make their own food (glucose).
To make glucose by photosynthesis, plants need four things: **light, water, carbon dioxide** and **chlorophyll.**

1 Sunlight is absorbed by chlorophyll, a green pigment within the chloroplasts.

2 Water enters a plant through its roots by osmosis and then travels to the leaves through tubes called xylem vessels.

3 Carbon dioxide enters leaves through the stomata.

4 The chlorophyll uses light energy to convert water and carbon dioxide into glucose and oxygen.

5 Oxygen, a by-product of photosynthesis, leaves the plant through the stomata.

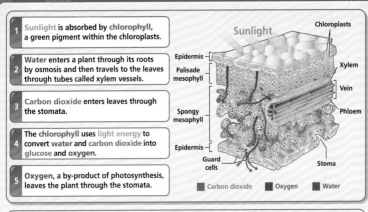

Sunlight — Chloroplasts — Epidermis — Palisade mesophyll — Xylem — Vein — Phloem — Spongy mesophyll — Epidermis — Guard cells — Stoma

■ Carbon dioxide ■ Oxygen ■ Water

Carbon dioxide $6CO_2$ **+** **Water** $6H_2O$ → *Light energy* / **Chlorophyll** → **Glucose** $C_6H_{12}O_6$ **+** **Oxygen** $6O_2$

Glucose is used in plants:

• For respiration • To make cell walls • To make proteins • For storage

Limiting Factors

The rate of photosynthesis is affected by light intensity, carbon dioxide concentration and temperature.

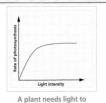

A plant needs light to photosynthesise. Increasing light intensity boosts the rate of photosynthesis to a certain level. Beyond this, other factors such as temperature and carbon dioxide limit the rate.

A plant needs carbon dioxide (CO_2) to photosynthesise. Increasing the concentration of CO_2 boosts the rate of photosynthesis to a certain level. Beyond this, other factors such as light intensity and temperature limit the rate.

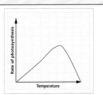

A plant cannot photosynthesise when the temperature is either below approximately 0°C or above 45°C.

SCIENTIFIC ENQUIRY

PLANNING

- Effective planning is essential.
- **Outline a plan for your investigation.**
- Decide what information you need to collect.
- **Decide what you will observe and measure.**
- Consider what apparatus and equipment you need.
- **Describe and assess any hazards in your investigation.**

INVESTIGATION

- Make sure your experiment is a fair test.
- **Obtain your information carefully through accurate observation and measurement.**
- Repeat your measurements and observations to ensure that the information is reliable.
- **Record your results clearly.**

ANALYSIS & EVALUATION

- Use the most effective way to present your results (table, graph, pie chart etc.).
- **Analyse the information. Are there any trends or patterns?**
- Draw conclusions from the results.
- **Consider the strength of your evidence. Can you make any improvements to the process? What would you do differently?**

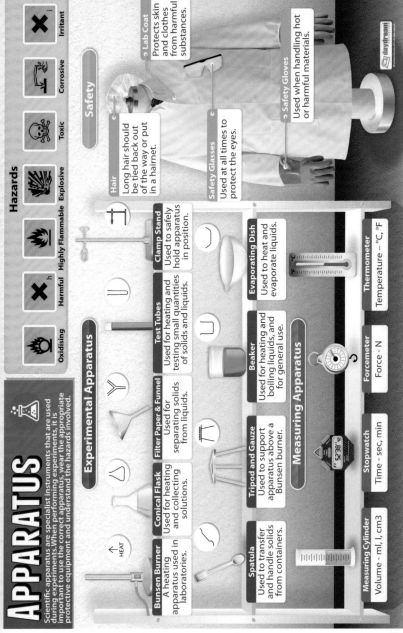

APPARATUS

Scientific apparatus are specialist instruments that are used during experiments. When performing experiments, it is important to use the correct apparatus, wear the appropriate protective equipment and understand the hazards involved.

Hazards

Oxidising	Harmful	Highly Flammable	Explosive
	Irritant	Corrosive	Toxic

Safety

Hair
Long hair should be tied back out of the way or put in a hairnet.

Safety Glasses
Used at all times to protect the eyes.

Lab Coat
Protects skin and clothes from harmful substances.

Safety Gloves
Used when handling hot or harmful materials.

Experimental Apparatus

Clamp Stand
Used to safely hold apparatus in position.

Test Tubes
Used for heating and testing small quantities of solids and liquids.

Filter Paper & Funnel
Used for separating solids from liquids.

Conical Flask
Used for heating and collecting solutions.

Bunsen Burner
A heating apparatus used in laboratories.

Spatula
Used to transfer and handle solids from containers.

Evaporating Dish
Used to heat and evaporate liquids.

Beaker
Used for heating and boiling liquids, and for general use.

Tripod and Gauze
Used to support apparatus above a Bunsen burner.

Measuring Apparatus

Thermometer
Temperature – °C, °F

Forcemeter
Force - N

Stopwatch
Time - sec, min

Measuring Cylinder
Volume - ml, l, cm3

SOLIDS

SNOOKER BALL

FORK

WOOD

PROPERTIES OF SOLIDS

Solids cannot easily be compressed.

Solids can be cut.

Solids are easily controlled.

Solids cannot flow.

Solids have definite volumes and definite shapes.

Look at the particles of a solid. It will help explain the above properties.

There are very strong forces of attraction between particles.

The particles are held tightly by strong forces and can hardly move.

Solids cannot easily be compressed because the particles are very close together.

There are lots of particles in a given volume.

LIQUIDS

WATER

PAINT

ORANGE JUICE

PROPERTIES OF LIQUIDS

Liquids cannot be cut.

Liquids take the shape of their containers.

Liquids are quite difficult to control.

Liquids have a definite volume.

Liquids cannot easily be compressed.

Liquids flow.

Look at the particles of a liquid. It will help explain the above properties.

There are quite strong forces of attraction between particles.

The particles move constantly because they are not held as strongly as in solids.

Liquids which completely fill a container cannot easily be compressed because the particles are held close together.

There are lots of particles in a given volume.

GASES

HELIUM

HYDROGEN

OXYGEN

PROPERTIES OF GASES

Gases do not have a definite volume.

Gases cannot be cut.

Gases fill any available space.

Gases can easily be compressed.

Gases are hard to control.

Gases flow easily.

Most gases are invisible and spread into open spaces.

Look at the particles of a gas. It will help explain the above properties.

There are very weak forces of attraction between the particles.

The particles are far apart and move freely.

Gases can easily be compressed because there is plenty of space for the particles to move into.

There are few particles in a given volume.

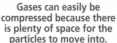

CHANGING MATERIALS

PHYSICAL CHANGES

A physical change affects the form of a substance but not its chemical composition. The change is **reversible**.

The diagram below shows how water changes state at different temperatures. Although there is a change in state, there is no change in mass or chemical composition.

SOLID

Ice
(10 grams)

Melting
when a solid changes into a liquid

HEAT IN

HEAT OUT

Freezing
when a liquid changes into a solid

LIQUID

Water
(10 grams)

Evaporation
when a liquid changes into a gas

HEAT IN

HEAT OUT

Condensation
when a gas changes into a liquid

GAS

Steam
(10 grams)

DISSOLVING

Dissolving occurs when a solid (solute) becomes incorporated in a liquid (solvent) to for a solution. The solid and liquid particles collide, causing the solid particles to break up and mix with the liquid particles.

Water
(solvent)

Sugar
(solute)

Sugar solution

The rate of dissolving can be increased by:

increasing the temperature   stirring the solution   crushing the solute

CHEMICAL CHANGES

A chemical change affects the chemical composition of a substance. The change is **irreversible**.

When **wood** burns, it turns to **ash**.

Ingredients are baked to make a **cake**.

Sand, **water** and **cement** are mixed to form **concrete**.

With chemical reactions, there is always a change in energy, usually heat. There is also usually a visible change, such as a change in colour or state.

SEPARATING MIXTURES

SIEVING

Can separate large particles from small particles.

SIEVE
- The sand and rock mixture is shaken through.
- The small holes in the sieve let the sand particles through and prevent the larger rocks from passing through.

FILTRATION

Can separate solids that are insoluble from a liquid.

FILTER PAPER
Sand gathers in the filter paper. Water passes through.

FUNNEL
Channels the water into the flask.

FLASK
Gathers the water after filtration.

EVAPORATION

Can separate solids that are soluble from a liquid.

SALT WATER

EVAPORATING DISH
Water evaporates into the air, leaving only the salt.

BUNSEN BURNER
Heats the salt water so that it boils and turns to steam.

CONDENSATION

Condensing is when water vapour changes into liquid water.

COLD SURFACE
The steam hits the surface and condenses into water droplets.

BUNSEN BURNER
Heats the water so that it boils and turns to steam.

CHROMATOGRAPHY

Can separate different colour dyes.

PAPER
- Spots of ink are placed on a pencil line.
- Solvent soaks up to the ink and each colour seeps upwards at a different rate.

SOLVENT
The paper is placed in the solvent which soaks up to the ink spots.

DISTILLATION

Can separate a solvent from a solution.

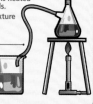

FLASK
- A mixture of liquids is heated from below and boils.
- The water in the mixture evaporates leaving the remainder.

CONDENSER
Steam condenses in the tube.

BEAKER
Pure, distilled water collects in the beaker.

ROCKS

Rocks are formed over millions of years in one of the following ways:

IGNEOUS

- Molten magma from the Earth's interior forms igneous rocks.

Extrusive Igneous Rocks

- These form when molten magma cools quickly on the surface producing fine-grained rocks such as basalt.

Intrusive Igneous Rocks

- These form when molten magma cools slowly underground producing large-grained rocks such as granite.

SEDIMENTARY

- Layers of sediment that have settled on the sea or lake bed over millions of years form sedimentary rocks.

- As the layers get heavier, water is squeezed out and the sediment forms rock.

- Some, such as limestone, contain fossils (plant and animal remains).

- Some, such as sandstone, contain fragments of rock eroded by the weather and transported down to the sea by rivers.

METAMORPHIC

- Metamorphic rocks are formed when heat or high pressure change existing rocks. They are usually tough and crystalline.

Contact metamorphism

- This occurs when rocks are altered due to heat from hot magma e.g. limestone to marble.

Region metamorphism

- This occurs when mountains are formed. Rocks are stressed and crushed so much they become a new rock e.g. mudstone to slate.

PERIODIC TABLE

The periodic table is all of the known elements in order of atomic number.

Legend: ■ Alkali metals ■ Alkaline earth metals ■ Transition metals ■ Other metals □ Other non-metals ■ Halogens ■ Noble gases ■ Rare earth metals

Transition metals

Metals

Non-metals

Period	Group 1	Group 2												Group 3	Group 4	Group 5	Group 6	Group 7	Group 0
1	1 H Hydrogen 1																		4 He Helium 2
2	7 Li Lithium 3	9 Be Beryllium 4												11 B Boron 5	12 C Carbon 6	14 N Nitrogen 7	16 O Oxygen 8	19 F Fluorine 9	20 Ne Neon 10
3	23 Na Sodium 11	24 Mg Magnesium 12												27 Al Aluminium 13	28 Si Silicon 14	31 P Phosphorus 15	32 S Sulphur 16	35.5 Cl Chlorine 17	40 Ar Argon 18
4	39 K Potassium 19	40 Ca Calcium 20	45 Sc Scandium 21	48 Ti Titanium 22	51 V Vanadium 23	52 Cr Chromium 24	55 Mn Manganese 25	56 Fe Iron 26	59 Co Cobalt 27	59 Ni Nickel 28	64 Cu Copper 29	65 Zn Zinc 30		70 Ga Gallium 31	73 Ge Germanium 32	75 As Arsenic 33	79 Se Selenium 34	80 Br Bromine 35	84 Kr Krypton 36
5	85 Rb Rubidium 37	88 Sr Strontium 38	89 Y Yttrium 39	91 Zr Zirconium 40	93 Nb Niobium 41	96 Mo Molybdenum 42	98 Tc Technetium 43	101 Ru Ruthenium 44	103 Rh Rhodium 45	106 Pd Palladium 46	108 Ag Silver 47	112 Cd Cadmium 48		115 In Indium 49	119 Sn Tin 50	122 Sb Antimony 51	128 Te Tellurium 52	127 I Iodine 53	131 Xe Xenon 54
6	133 Cs Caesium 55	137 Ba Barium 56	139 La* Lanthanum 57	178.5 Hf Hafnium 72	181 Ta Tantalum 73	184 W Tungsten 74	186 Re Rhenium 75	190 Os Osmium 76	192 Ir Iridium 77	195 Pt Platinum 78	197 Au Gold 79	201 Hg Mercury 80		204 Tl Thallium 81	207 Pb Lead 82	209 Bi Bismuth 83	209 Po Polonium 84	210 At Astatine 85	222 Rn Radon 86
7	223 Fr Francium 87	226 Ra Radium 88	227 Ac** Actinium 89	261 Rf Rutherfordium 104	262 Db Dubnium 105	266 Sg Seaborgium 106	264 Bh Bohrium 107	269 Hs Hassium 108	268 Mt Meitnerium 109	281 Ds Darmstadtium 110	272 Rg Roentgenium 111								

Lanthanides

140 Ce Cerium 58	141 Pr Praseodymium 59	144 Nd Neodymium 60	145 Pm Promethium 61	150 Sm Samarium 62	152 Eu Europium 63	157 Gd Gadolinium 64	159 Tb Terbium 65	162.5 Dy Dysprosium 66	165 Ho Holmium 67	167 Er Erbium 68	169 Tm Thulium 69	173 Yb Ytterbium 70	175 Lu Lutetium 71

Actinides

232 Th Thorium 90	231 Pa Protactinium 91	238 U Uranium 92	237 Np Neptunium 93	243 Pu Plutonium 94	241 Am Americium 95	247 Cm Curium 96	247 Bk Berkelium 97	251 Cf Californium 98	252 Es Einsteinium 99	257 Fm Fermium 100	258 Md Mendelevium 101	259 No Nobelium 102	260 Lr Lawrencium 103

GROUPS
The vertical columns, called groups, contain elements with similar properties.

PERIODS
The horizontal rows, called periods, contain elements displaying a gradual change in properties.

METAL/NON-METAL
The bold red line on the main diagram divides metals on the left from non-metals on the right.

KEY

65
Zn
30

Atomic mass — Symbol — Name — Atomic number

PHYSICAL UNITS

	QUANTITY	NAME	SYMBOL
	ENERGY	Joules	J
	MOMENT	Newton-metres	Nm
	SPEED	metres per sec	m/s
	TIME	seconds	s
	WEIGHT	Newtons	N
	AREA	square metres	m^2
	DISTANCE	metres	m
	MASS	kilograms	kg
	VOLUME	cubic metres	m^3
	DENSITY	kg per m^3	kg/m^3
	FORCE	Newtons	N
	PRESSURE	Pascals	Pa (N/m^2)
	CURRENT	Amperes	A
	POTENTIAL DIFFERENCE	Volts	V
	RESISTANCE	Ohms	Ω
	TEMPERATURE	degrees Celsius	°C

ELECTRICAL CIRCUITS

Electric current is the flow of charge around a circuit.

CIRCUIT

Electric current can only flow if there is a complete circuit. Any gaps will stop the current flowing.

- In a circuit, a battery provides the energy (voltage) to push charge around the circuit. A battery is made up of numerous connected cells.

- Ammeters are used to measure electric current.

- Current cannot be used up.

CONVENTIONAL CURRENT

Conventional current is shown on circuits as flowing from positive to negative. However, the moving electrons actually have a negative charge and flow in the opposite direction to conventional current.

SERIES CIRCUIT

The electrics in computers, stereos and televisions contain series circuits.

CLOSED CIRCUIT

OPEN CIRCUIT

- The current is the same anywhere in this circuit, as the current can only take one path.

- The current can be turned on (switch closed) or off (switch open).

- The more cells in the circuit, the brighter the bulbs will be.

- The more bulbs there are in the circuit, the more resistance against the current. Therefore, the bulbs will be dimmer.

PARALLEL CIRCUIT

The mains electricity in a house is a parallel circuit, allowing appliances to be used independently.

OPEN

CLOSED

OPEN

OPEN

- The current takes more than one path.

- The current joins back up again on its way back to the battery. Therefore, the current is the same at the start and at the end of the circuit.

- Switches can be turned on or off to allow or restrict the flow to one or more parts of the circuit.

- Remember: Current is not used up.

CIRCUIT SYMBOLS

Electrical circuit diagrams can sometimes look confusing.
Here is an explanation of the most commonly used symbols.

Cell

A cell is a source of electrical energy.

Battery

A battery contains numerous connected cells that produce electrical energy.

Switch

Closed
Open
A switch can be turned on (closed) to let current flow or turned off (open) to stop current flow.

Bulb / Lamp

A bulb/lamp will light up only when it is in a circuit that is complete.

Motor

A motor turns current into motion, for example, in a hair dryer.

LED

A Light-Emitting Diode (LED) converts electrical energy into light energy.

Resistor

A fixed resistor controls the amount of current in a circuit.

Variable Resistor

A variable resistor can be adjusted to control the amount of current in a circuit.

Voltmeter

A voltmeter is used to measure the potential difference between two points in an electrical circuit.

Ammeter

An ammeter is used to measure current.

Buzzer

A buzzer turns current into sound.

Diode

A diode allows current to flow in one direction only and is normally used to prevent damage to other components.

LDR

A Light-Dependent Resistor (LDR) adapts to the amount of light it receives. As light intensity increases, resistance decreases.

Thermistor

A thermistor is a type of resistor. Its resistance varies significantly with temperature.

FORCES

Forces are pushes or pulls.
Forces always have a direction in which they act.
We measure force in newtons - N.

**The man pushes the trolley
away from him.**

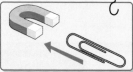

**The force on the paper clip
is towards the magnet.**

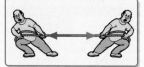

balanced force = no acceleration

unbalanced force = acceleration

What other forces are in these diagrams?

REMEMBER FORCES MAKE THINGS...

move

turn

go faster

slow down

change direction

change shape

GRAVITY is a force. It keeps us on the ground but also determines the movement of the stars and planets. The gravitational pull of the Earth attracts things to the centre of the Earth.

FRICTION

Friction occurs when two surfaces meet and rub against each other.
Friction slows a moving object, but can help control the movement.

ROUGH SURFACES

Rough surfaces slow moving objects but can be helpful.

The friction between the rough gravel and the tyres slows the racing car down.

The friction between his boots and the rock surface helps the climber keep his grip.

HEAT

Friction produces heat.

Rubbing your hands together produces heat.

Rubbing two pieces of wood together can produce enough heat to create flames.

AIR RESISTANCE

Air resistance can affect motion: it can slow things down.

Gravity pulls this person down.

A small area means low air resistance and therefore a fast fall.

A large area means more air resistance and therefore a slower fall.

You can reduce air resistance by changing shape to become more streamlined.

The ski jumper tucks his arms in to reduce air resistance.

The cyclist tucks his head down to reduce air resistance.

This car is designed to be smooth and streamlined so that it goes fast.

LIGHT REFLECTION,
REFRACTION AND DISPERSION

REFLECTION

When light hits a surface, it is reflected. Most surfaces scatter light in all directions. Mirrors and other shiny objects with smooth surfaces reflect light in a specific direction, giving a clear reflection.

scattered light
paper

reflected light
mirror

When a light ray hits a surface, we call it an incident ray. The light reflected off the surface is called a reflected ray.

incident ray   reflected ray

the angle of incidence = the angle of reflection
angle i = angle r

REFRACTION

When light travels from one medium to another, it changes direction. This is called **refraction**. This happens because light travels at different speeds in different materials.

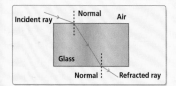

Incident ray   Normal   Air

Glass

Normal   Refracted ray

When moving from a **less dense** medium to a **denser** medium, light bends **towards the normal** because it slows down.

When moving from a **denser** medium to a **less dense** medium, light bends **away from the normal** because it speeds up.

Light is not refracted if it travels along the **normal line at 90°**.

DISPERSION

White light is actually made up of a mixture of colours. When light hits a prism, it gets dispersed into a rainbow of colours known as a spectrum. This is caused by **refraction**.

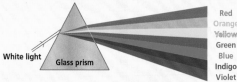

White light   Glass prism

Red
Orange
Yellow
Green
Blue
Indigo
Violet

Remember: Richard Of York Gave Battle In Vain

AMPLITUDE AND PITCH

AMPLITUDE

Sound is a form of energy.

Low energy = quiet sound

High energy = loud sound

Intensity of sound is indicated by the height (amplitude) of the wave on an oscilloscope.

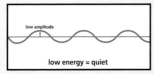

low amplitude

low energy = quiet

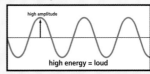

high amplitude

high energy = loud

The further away you are from the source of the sound, the quieter the sound gets. This is because it spreads out and becomes dispersed.

PITCH

Pitch defines how high or low a note sounds.

For strings that are:

shorter
thinner } = high pitch
tighter

For strings that are:

longer
thicker } = low pitch
looser

Frequency, which measures the pitch of a note, is shown by the number of vibrations per second on an oscilloscope.

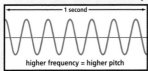

1 second

higher frequency = higher pitch

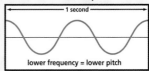

1 second

lower frequency = lower pitch

We measure sound frequency in hertz (Hz).

ENERGY RESOURCES

The Sun is the source of all energy resources.

TYPES OF ENERGY

NON-RENEWABLE ENERGY
(fossil fuels)

RENEWABLE ENERGY

Coal

Natural Gas

Oil

Solar (Sun)

Wind

Hydro

Energy from fossil fuels is **non-renewable**. Fossil fuel will eventually run out as they take millions of years to reform. Energy from **renewable** sources will never run out however much we use them.

FOSSIL FUELS

Fossil fuels are fuels formed from the remains of dead plants and animals compressed over millions of years. Coal, Oil and Natural Gas are all fossil fuels.

Plants and animals used the sun's energy to live. When they died, they became buried in mud.

The mud turned to rock. The dead plants became coal and the dead animals oil and gas.

Coal is burnt to generate electricity. Oil and gas are used for heating and fuel for vehicles.

GREENHOUSE EFFECT

The main disadvantage of using fossil fuels for energy is that it harms the environment.

- Burning any fossil fuel produces carbon dioxide, which contributes to the 'greenhouse effect'.
- Carbon dioxide acts like a blanket which keeps heat in.
- Scientists believe that this is causing the polar ice caps to melt and is changing our climate.

THE EARTH

The Earth is the third planet from the Sun and the fifth largest in the solar system.

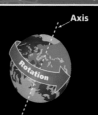

The Earth spins on its axis approximately once every 24 hours.

Axis

1 rotation = 24 hours = 1 day

The Earth orbits the Sun once every 365.25 days. This means that the Earth spins 365.25 times in every orbit of the Sun.

The Sun

1 orbit = 365.25 days* = 1 year

*This is rounded to 365 days and an extra day (29th February) is added every four years. Once in a long while, a leap year is skipped because the Earth's orbit is actually 365.242 days.

DAY AND NIGHT

As the Earth spins, different parts face the Sun.
At any time, half of the Earth faces the sun and half faces away.

Axis

DAY

Equator

NIGHT

The half facing the Sun experiences day-time.
The half facing away from the Sun experiences night-time.

EARTH'S SEASONS

The tilted axis of Earth's rotation around the Sun causes the seasons.
As the Earth completes one orbit of the Sun, different parts tilt towards and away from the Sun.

The Seasons

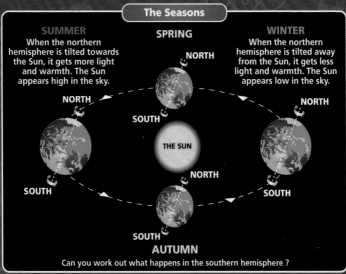

SUMMER
When the northern hemisphere is tilted towards the Sun, it gets more light and warmth. The Sun appears high in the sky.

SPRING

WINTER
When the northern hemisphere is tilted away from the Sun, it gets less light and warmth. The Sun appears low in the sky.

NORTH

SOUTH

NORTH

SOUTH

THE SUN

NORTH

NORTH

SOUTH

SOUTH

AUTUMN

Can you work out what happens in the southern hemisphere ?

How it Works

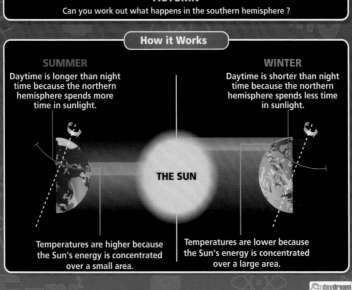

SUMMER
Daytime is longer than night time because the northern hemisphere spends more time in sunlight.

WINTER
Daytime is shorter than night time because the northern hemisphere spends less time in sunlight.

THE SUN

Temperatures are higher because the Sun's energy is concentrated over a small area.

Temperatures are lower because the Sun's energy is concentrated over a large area.

daydream

THE SOLAR SYSTEM

All planets orbit continuously around the Sun. The Sun's gravitational force determines their movement. The orbital time of each planet depends on its distance from the Sun.

Diagram not to scale.

	SUN	MERCURY	VENUS	EARTH	MARS	JUPITER	SATURN	URANUS	NEPTUNE	PLUTO*
Distance from the Sun		60 million km	108 million km	149.6 million km	228 million km	778 million km	1,427 million km	2,870 million km	4,497 million km	5,900 million km
Orbital time		88 days	225 days	365.25 days	687 days	12 years	30 years	84 years	165 years	250 years
Diameter		4,878 km	12,104 km	12,756 km	6,794 km	142,800 km	120,000 km	51,800 km	49,500 km	2,500 km

*Pluto was re-classified as a 'dwarf planet' on August 24th 2006 by the International Astronomical Union (IAU).

THE SUN

MERCURY VENUS EARTH MARS JUPITER SATURN URANUS NEPTUNE PLUTO

daydream

Like our Pocket Posters?

...then you'll love our award-winning A1 Posters and Interactive Content Packs.

A1 Posters

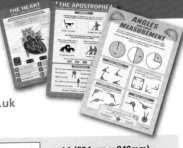

All of the posters contained in this book are available as A1 Posters, from only £4.50.

Visit **www.daydreameducation.co.uk** to see our full range of Posters.

| Paper: from £4.50 | Laminated: from £7.50 |

A1 (594mm x 840mm)

Interactive Content Packs

FROM ONLY £8 SITE LICENCE

See our Pocket Posters come to life with our award-winning Interactive Content Packs.

The Content Packs are ideal for use on whiteboards, projectors, individual PCs and Macs.

Approved by

Also available for your VLE (learning platform)

Visit **www.daydreameducation.co.uk** for more information and your **FREE** downloadable Content Packs worth up to £250!